CONSUMER MATHEMATICS 5
CONSTRUCTION AND
BUILDING TRADES

CONTENTS

Author: Thomas W. Hazard, Ph.D.
Editor-in-Chief: Richard W. Wheeler, M.A.ED.
Editor: Stephany L. Sykes
Consulting Editor: Robert L. Zenor, M.A. M.S.
Illustrator: Thomas R. Rush

AOP

804 N. 2nd Ave. E.   Rock Rapids, IA 51246-1759   800-622-3070   www.aop.com

CONSTRUCTION AND BUILDING TRADES

The construction and building trades constitute a very important component of this nation's economic sector. For anyone seeking a job in any of a number of trades, the ability to handle basic mathematics, including the use of the metric system, is an important asset. Also, since so much of the material specifications used in construction and repair work are in tabular form, an understanding of their application is essential to estimating, ordering, and purchasing the required materials for whatever job one may have.

Practical examples are included in this LIFEPAC that will assist the student in perfecting those mathematical skills relevant to the construction and building trades. The branch of mathematics most appropriate is that dealing with finding lengths, areas, and volumes, known as *mensuration*. This LIFEPAC will enable you to acquire and perfect mensuration skills and will demonstrate some simple yet important applications.

OBJECTIVES

Read these objectives. The objectives tell you what you will be able to do when you have successfully completed this LIFEPAC.

When you have finished this LIFEPAC, you should be able

1. To identify basic units of the metric system,

2. To use metric prefixes based upon powers of ten,

3. To convert English units to the metric system,

4. To identify plane geometric figures,

5. To compute the areas of geometric figures,

6. To estimate building materials requirements,

7. To identify solid geometric figures,

8. To compute volumes of liquids and solids given appropriate dimensions, and

9. To estimate building materials requirements based on volume.

Survey the LIFEPAC. Ask yourself some questions about this study. Write your questions here.

_____

_____

_____

_____

_____

_____

_____

_____

_____

I. MEASUREMENT SYSTEMS	**OBJECTIVES**
	1. To identify basic units of the metric system.
	2. To use metric prefixes based upon powers of ten.
	3. To convert English units to the metric system.

Measurements are essential for satisfactory completion of practically all tasks associated with the construction and building trades. Understanding the terms associated with the various measurements is an important element of job performance. Ability to work in either the United States (nonmetric) or the international (metric) systems is necessary because you will find measurements employing both systems in use today. The nonmetric system used in the United States today is called the English system, because it was derived from ancient English measurements. Today, however, England uses the metric system.

METRIC SYSTEM

The modern metric system is known as the *International System of Units*. The name *International System of Units* with the international abbreviation (SI) was given to the system by the General Conference on Weights and Measures in 1960.

DEFINITION

The *International System of Units* is a decimal system, based on the number ten, of weights and measures, employing grams, meters, liters, and other units.

Seven Basic units have been established as the *International System of Units*:

    The meter (m) for length;
    The kilogram (kg) for mass;
    The second (s) for time;
    The Kelvin (K) or Celsius (C) degree for temperature;
    The mole (mol) for the amount of a substance;
    The ampere (A) for electric current; and
    The candela (cd) for luminous intensity.

These units are the standard, and all other units may be obtained from them by derivation. If we wish to show multiples of these basic units, we simply attach a prefix to the original name to indicate whether we are multiplying or dividing the basic unit and by how much. If the prefix (mega-) ends in the same letter that the basic unit (ampere) begins in, we separate the words with a hyphen: mega-ampere.

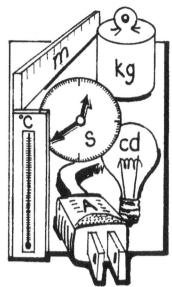

PROCEDURE

Metric prefixes are derived from the Greek language and are assigned to a basic unit according to a particular power of 10.

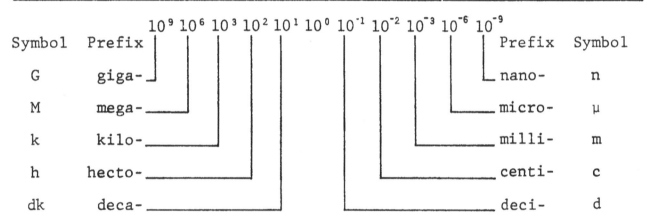

Symbol	Prefix										Prefix	Symbol
		10^9	10^6	10^3	10^2	10^1	10^0	10^{-1}	10^{-2}	10^{-3}	10^{-6}	10^{-9}		
G	giga-													nano-	n
M	mega-												micro-	μ
k	kilo-											milli-	m
h	hecto-										centi-	c
dk	deca-									deci-	d

Powers of Ten

Model 1: Express $\frac{1}{1,000}$ gram using the appropriate prefix.

From the Powers of Ten prefix table, we find *milli-* corresponding to 10^{-3}. Therefore, $\frac{1}{1,000}$ gram may be expressed as 1 milligram, or 1 mg.

Model 2: Express 10,000 meters in an equivalent form using the appropriate prefix.

$$10,000 = 10^4 \text{ or } 10 \times 10^3$$

From the Powers of Ten prefix table, we find that 10^3 corresponds to the prefix *kilo-*. Hence, 10×10^3 meters may be written as 10 kilometers, or 10 km.

Express the following measurements with the appropriate prefixes and symbols.

1.1 $\frac{1}{10}$ meter   _____

1.2   100 liters   _____

1.3 $\frac{1}{1,000,000}$ gram   _____

1.4   1,000 seconds   _____

1.5   1,000,000 amperes   _____

1.6 10^9 candelas   _____

1.7   10,000 grams   _____

1.8 $\frac{1}{500,000}$ liter   _____

1.9   1 nanosecond   _____

1.10   1 hectometer   _____

1.11   1 milliampere   _____

1.12   1 megaton   _____

Once you get used to the metric system, you are going to find it much easier to use in everyday activities. It will ease mathematical problems greatly because of its basis in the decimal system. Just think how much simpler you can make change and figure costs because one cent is $\frac{1}{100}$ of a dollar and a dime is $\frac{1}{10}$ of a dollar; instead of having to convert 120 cents to a dollar, or 3 quarters to a dollar, such as might be the case if our money system were based upon our current system of inches, feet, and yards.

To put this statement to a test, let us consider a rather routine problem of laying a brick patio.

ENGLISH SYSTEM	METRIC SYSTEM
Problem: How many bricks $3\frac{3}{4}$" x 8" will cover a patio 16'3" wide by 19'8" long?	Problem: How many bricks 9.5 cm x 20 cm will cover a patio 5 meters wide by 6 meters long?
Step 1. Convert feet to inches:	Step 1. Find the area of the patio:
a. 16 ft. = 16 x 12 = 192 in. b. 19 ft. = 19 x 12 = 228 in.	(5 x 100)(6 x 100) = 300,000 cm²
Step 2. Find total length and width of patio:	Step 2. Find the area of each brick:
a. 192 in. + 3 in. = 195 in. b. 228 in. + 8 in. = 236 in.	9.5 x 20 = 190 cm²
Step 3. Find the area of the patio:	Step 3. Divide the patio area by the brick area to get the number of bricks needed:
195 x 236 = 46,020 in.²	300,000 ÷ 190 = 1,578.9 or 1,579 bricks, rounded off
Step 4. Find the area of each brick:	
$3\frac{3}{4}$" x 8" = 30 in.²	
Step 5. Divide the patio area by the brick area to get the number of bricks needed:	
46,020 ÷ 30 = 1,534 bricks	

The fact that the answers are slightly different is not important--the corresponding measurements used in the United States and metric systems are not exactly equivalent. The important thing is that we took only three steps to arrive at an answer using the metric system in comparison to five steps, and several substeps, in the English system of measurement. In addition, the numbers to work with were much more complex in the English system.

CONVERSION PROCEDURES

Conversion of English units of length to metric units may be accomplished through the application of the following procedure and the use of the conversion table.

```
┌─────────────────────────────────────────────────────────────────────────┐
│ PROCEDURE                                                                 │
│                                                                           │
│ To convert an English unit of length to the equivalent metric            │
│ unit of length, multiply the length by the appropriate con-              │
│ version number.  Conversely, to convert a metric unit of                 │
│ length to the equivalent English unit of length, multiply the            │
│ length by the reciprocal of the appropriate conversion number:           │
│       English length x conversion number = metric length.                │
│                              1                                            │
│       Metric length x ──────────────────── = English length.             │
│                        conversion number                                 │
└─────────────────────────────────────────────────────────────────────────┘
```

```
╔═══════════════════════════════════════════════════════════════════════╗
║              Length Conversion Number Table                             ║
║                                                                         ║
║  English Length          Conversion Number          Metric Length      ║
╚═══════════════════════════════════════════════════════════════════════╝
```

English Length	Conversion Number	Metric Length
miles	1.609	kilometers
miles	1,609	meters
yards	9.144×10^{-4}	kilometers
yards	9.144×10^{-1}	meters
feet	3.048×10^{-1}	meters
feet	30.48	centimeters
inches	2.54×10^{-2}	meters
inches	2.54	centimeters
inches	25.4	millimeters

Model 1: How many kilometers in 52 miles?

From the conversion number table,
you can find the number of kilometers by multiplying the number
of miles given by 1.609. Therefore,
52 x 1.609 = 83.67 kilometers.

Model 2: How many feet in 14 meters?

From the procedure rule given, we
know that to convert metric units
to English units, we must multiply
the metric units given by the reciprocal
of the appropriate conversion number
found in the table. Since
meters = feet x 3.048×10^{-1},
feet = meters x $\frac{1}{0.3048}$ = meters x 3.281.
Therefore, 14 x 3.281 = 45.93 feet.

■■■■ Convert the following unit lengths as indicated.

1.13   Convert $10\frac{1}{2}$ inches to millimeters.   _____

1.14   Convert 18 kilometers to miles.   _____

1.15   Convert 100 yards to meters.   _____

1.16   Convert 600 miles per hour to km per hr. _____

■■■■ Select the best answer from the series of possible answers provided after each of the following unit length problems.

1.17 To find the number of centimeters in 10 inches, multiply the number of inches given (10) by _____.

   a. 3.04   b. 2.54   c. 2.78   d. 2.44

1.18 To find the number of inches in 3.5 meters, multiply the number of meters given (3.5) by _____.

   a. 36   b. 25.4   c. 39.4   d. 0.305

1.19 To find the number of miles in 100 kilometers, _____.

   a. divide 100 by 1.609   c. multiply 100 by 3.281
   b. multiply 100 by 1.609   d. divide 100 by 3.281

Conversion of English units of area to metric units may be accomplished through the application of the following procedure and the use of the conversion table.

PROCEDURE

To convert an English unit of area to the equivalent metric unit of area, multiply the English area by the appropriate conversion number. Conversely, to convert a metric unit of area to its equivalent English unit, multiply the metric area by the reciprocal of the appropriate conversion number:

English area x conversion number = metric area.

Metric area x $\dfrac{1}{\text{conversion number}}$ = English area.

Area Conversion Number Table		
English Area	Conversion Number	Metric Area
square miles	2.59	square kilometers
square miles	259	hectares
acres	4.05×10^{-3}	square kilometers
acres	4.05×10^{-1}	hectares
square yards	8.36×10^{-1}	square meters
square feet	9.29×10^{-2}	square meters
square inches	6.45	square centimeters

7

Model 1: How many square meters are in a
          house whose area is 1,750 square feet?

          From the procedure rule given, we know
          that we find the conversion number by
          which square feet can be converted to
          square meters and then we multiply the
          square feet given by this number to
          obtain the number of square meters.
          Therefore, $1{,}750 \times 9.29 \times 10^{-2} = 162.58$ m².

Model 2: A piece of cloth measuring 6" by 5"
          contains 30 in.² of material. How many
          square centimeters of material are in
          this cloth?

          square centimeters = square inches x 6.45
          Therefore, $30 \times 6.45 = 193.5$ cm².

▬▬▬ Convert the following unit areas as indicated.

1.20   Convert 125 square yards to square meters.   _____

1.21   Convert 9½ square centimeters to square
       inches.   _____

1.22   Convert 16 square kilometers to acres.   _____

1.23   A search plane covers 50 square miles of
       countryside. How many hectares does the
       plane search?   _____

▬▬▬ Write *true* or *false*.

1.24   _____ To convert 5 square meters to square yards, multiply
               5 by 1.196.

1.25   _____ To convert 3 square feet to square centimeters,
               multiply 3 by 9.29×10^{-2}.

1.26   _____ To convert 50 hectares to acres, divide 50 by
               4.05×10^{-1}.

1.27   _____ To determine the number of square centimeters in 8
               square inches, multiply 8 by 6.45.

     English units of volume can be converted to
metric units through the application of the
following procedure and the use of the conversion
table.

```
PROCEDURE

To convert an English unit of volume to its equivalent metric
unit of volume, multiply the English volume by the appropriate
conversion number.  Conversely, to convert a metric unit of
volume to its corresponding English unit, multiply the metric
unit given by the reciprocal of the appropriate conversion
number:

   English unit of volume x conversion number = metric volume.

   Metric unit of volume x ────────1──────── = English volume.
                            conversion number
```

Volume Conversion Number Table

English Volume	Conversion Number	Metric Volume
cubic yards	7.645×10^{-1}	cubic meters
cubic feet	2.832×10^{-2}	cubic meters
fluid ounces	29.574	cubic centimeters
pints (liquid)*	473.18	cubic centimeters
quarts (liquid)	946.36	cubic centimeters
pints (liquid)	4.732×10^{-1}	liters
quarts (liquid)	9.463×10^{-1}	liters
gallons (liquid)	3.785	liters

```
*To find the conversion number for dry equivalent volume,
 multiply the appropriate conversion number for the liquid
 volume by 1.164.  In other words, to convert 1 pint dry
 to cubic centimeters, the proper conversion number is
 473.18 x 1.164, or 550.8.
```

Model 1: Convert 10 gallons of gasoline to
          liters.

          Liters (liquid) = U.S. gallons x 3.785.
          Therefore, 10 x 3.785 = 37.85 liters.

Model 2: Convert 15 cubic meters of cement
          to cubic yards.

          Cubic yards = cubic meters x $\dfrac{1}{7.645 \times 10^{-1}}$.

          Therefore, $15 \times \dfrac{1}{7.645 \times 10^{-1}} = 19.62$ cu. yds.

██████ Convert the following unit volumes as indicated.

1.28   Convert 25 pints (liquid) to liters.   _____

1.29   Convert 1 quart (liquid) to cubic centimeters. _____

1.30   Convert 6 cubic centimeters to fluid ounces. _____

1.31   Convert 4 quarts (dry) to liters.   _____

Match the following unit volumes with the most appropriate converted unit volume.

1.32 _____ 10 liters

1.33 _____ 5 cubic feet

1.34 _____ 7 cubic yards

1.35 _____ 3 liters

a. 0.14 cubic meters

b. 5.35 cubic meters

c. 21.1 quarts

d. 6.34 pints

e. 2.64 gallons

English units of weight can be converted to metric units through the application of the following procedure and the use of the conversion table.

PROCEDURE

To convert an English unit of weight to its equivalent metric unit of weight, multiply the English weight by the appropriate conversion number. Conversely, to convert the metric unit of weight to its corresponding English unit, multiply the metric unit given by the reciprocal of the appropriate conversion number:

English unit of weight x conversion number = metric weight.

Metric unit of weight x $\dfrac{1}{\text{conversion number}}$ = English weight.

Weight Conversion Number Table

English Weight	Conversion Number	Metric Weight
ounces	28.35	grams
ounces	28.35×10^{-2}	kilograms
grains	64.798	milligrams
pounds	453.59	grams
pounds	4.536×10^{-4}	metric tons
pounds	4.536×10^{-1}	kilograms
tons (short)	9.072×10^{-1}	metric tons
tons (short)	907.2	kilograms

Model 1: Convert 250 pounds to kilograms.

Kilograms = pounds x 4.536×10^{-1}.

Therefore, $250 \times 4.536 \times 10^{-1} = 113.4$ kilograms.

Model 2: How many ounces are in 50 grams?
Ounces = grams x $\frac{1}{28.35}$. Therefore,
50 x $\frac{1}{28.35}$ = 1.76 ounces.

███████ Convert the following unit weights as indicated.

1.36   Convert 15 English tons (short) to metric tons.   _____

1.37   Convert 150 grains to milligrams.   _____

1.38   Convert 100 kilograms to pounds.   _____

1.39   What is the weight in kilograms of a 65 lb. bag of cement?   _____

English units of temperature can be converted to metric units through the application of the following procedure.

PROCEDURE

To convert an English unit of temperature, expressed in Fahrenheit degrees, to the equivalent metric unit of temperature, expressed in Celsius degrees, subtract 32 from the Fahrenheit temperature and multiply the result by the fraction $\frac{5}{9}$. Conversely, to convert Celsius degrees to Fahrenheit degrees, multiply the Celsius temperature by $\frac{9}{5}$ and add 32 to the result:

$$°C = (°F - 32) \times \frac{5}{9}. \qquad °F = \frac{9}{5} \times °C + 32.$$

Model 1: Convert 32°F to the Celsius scale.
$°C = \frac{5}{9} \times (°F - 32) = \frac{5}{9} \times (32 - 32)$.
Therefore, $°C = 0$.

Model 2: The reading on a Celsius thermometer is 30° C. What is the reading on a Fahrenheit thermometer?
$°F = \frac{9}{5} \times °C + 32 = \frac{9}{5} \times 30 + 32$.
Therefore, $°F = 86$.

11

■■■■■ Convert the following temperatures as indicated.

1.40   Convert 96°F to °C.   _____

1.41   Convert 10°C to °F.   _____

1.42   Convert 2°C to °F.   _____

REVIEW   Review the material in this section in preparation for the Self Test. The Self Test will check your mastery of this particular section. The items missed on this Self Test will indicate specific areas where restudy is needed for mastery.

SELF TEST 1

Express the following measurements with the appropriate prefixes and symbols (each answer, 2 points).

1.01 $\dfrac{1}{10,000}$ meter   _____

1.02   1,000,000 liters   _____

1.03 $\dfrac{1}{1,000,000}$ ampere   _____

1.04   50,000 grams   _____

1.05 $\dfrac{1}{1,000,000,000}$ second   _____

Convert the following unit lengths as indicated (each answer, 3 points).

1.06   Convert 15,000 feet to kilometers.   _____

1.07   Convert 300 centimeters to yards.   _____

1.08   Convert 440 yards to meters.   _____

1.09   Convert 25½ inches to centimeters.   _____

1.010   Convert 30,000 microns (a micron is one   _____
        millionth of a meter) to inches.

Convert the following unit areas as indicated (each answer, 3 points).

1.011   Convert 40 in.^{2} to cm^2.   _____

1.012   Convert 40,000 ft.^{2} to hectares   _____
        (1 hectare = 10,000 m^2).
1.013   Convert 5 cm^2 to in.^{2} _____

12

1.014 Convert 10 mi.² to hectares. _____

1.015 Convert 90 yd.² to m². _____

Convert the following unit volumes as indicated (each answer, 3 points).

1.016 Convert 10 ft.³ to m³. _____

1.017 Convert 1,500 cm³ to quarts (liquid). _____

1.018 Convert 17 gallons to liters. _____

1.019 Convert 3.5 liters to gallons. _____

1.020 Convert 50 quarts to liters. _____

Convert the following unit weights as indicated (each answer, 3 points).

1.021 Convert 6,000 grams to pounds. _____

1.022 Convert 450 grains to grams. _____

1.023 Convert 85 kilograms to pounds. _____

1.024 Convert $\frac{3}{4}$ ton (short) to metric tons. _____

1.025 Convert 6,000 kilograms to English tons. _____

Match the following temperatures in the left column with the appropriate temperatures on the right (each answer, 2 points).

1.026 _____ 98.6°F   a. 1,649°C

1.027 _____ 69.98°F   b. 2,800°C

1.028 _____ 5,072°F   c. 37°C

1.029 _____ 3,000°F   d. 21.1°C

1.030 _____ 110°F   e. 43.3°C

64 / 80

Score _____
Teacher check _____
                Initial   Date

13

II. AREA COMPUTATIONS AND APPLICATIONS

OBJECTIVES

4. To identify plane geometric figures.
5. To compute the areas of geometric figures.
6. To estimate building materials requirements.

Frequently a builder or tradesman needs to compute the areas of the more common two-dimensional geometric figures such as rectangles, triangles, and circles. Skill in computing areas enables one to estimate the building materials required to complete the particular task undertaken. Once the amount of materials is known, calculating the costs of the materials needed becomes a relatively easy problem since unit cost data are readily available from which the materials cost estimate can be figured.

PLANE FIGURES WITH STRAIGHT BOUNDARIES

This section will cover triangles and rectangles. These figures are among the most frequently encountered figures in construction.

DEFINITIONS

A *triangle* is a plane geometric figure bounded by three sides and enclosed by three angles. Although three major classifications of triangles exist--scalene, right, and isosceles--only the latter two are of common occurrence in the building trades, particularly in house construction.

Base of a triangle: Any side of the triangle.

Altitude of a triangle: The distance of a line drawn perpendicular from the base to the intersection of the two other sides.

Area of a triangle: $A = \frac{1}{2}bh$, where A stands for the area, b stands for the length of the base, and h stands for the altitude.

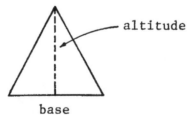

altitude

base

In a right triangle, one of the angles formed by the inter-section of two adjacent sides is a 90° right angle. With such a triangle the square of the side opposite the right angle is equal to the sum of the squares of the other two sides.

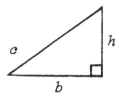

Therefore, in the right triangle shown, $c^2 = b^2 + h^2$.

Model 1: Determine the area of a triangle whose base is 12 cm and whose altitude is 8 cm.

$A = \frac{1}{2}bh = \frac{1}{2}(12 \text{ cm})(8 \text{ cm})$.

Therefore, $A = 48 \text{ cm}^2$.

Model 2: Given the following triangle, determine its area:

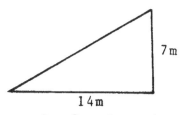

Since the angle forming the two sides with measured lengths is 90°, or a right angle, the 7 meters line is perpendicular to the 14 meters line, and, hence, is the altitude of the triangle by definition.

$A = \frac{1}{2}bh = \frac{1}{2}(14 \text{ m})(7 \text{ m})$.

Therefore, $A = 49 \text{ m}^2$

Model 3: Given an isosceles triangle with the two equal sides each measuring 5 cm and the base measuring 8 cm, compute the total area.

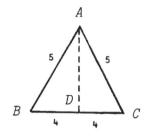

15

From vertex A draw a line perpendicular to base BC. By definition of an isosceles triangle, the perpendicular will bisect the base line, so that $BD = DC = 4$ cm.

Since $AB^2 = BD^2 + AD^2$,

$$AD^2 = AB^2 - BD^2 = 5^2 - 4^2.$$

$$AD^2 = 25 - 16 = 9.$$

Therefore, $AD = \sqrt{9} = 3$.

A of triangle $ABC = \frac{1}{2}bh = \frac{1}{2}(8)(3)$.

Therefore, $A = 12$ cm^2.

■■■ Compute the areas of the following triangles.

2.1 $b = 16.5$ in.; $h = 7.5$ in.   _____

2.2

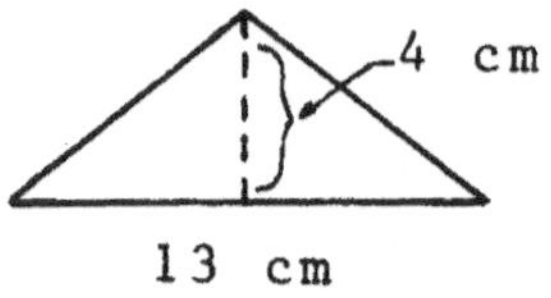

13 cm   4 cm

                                                          _____

2.3 $b = 20$ in.; $h = 4$ in. (express answer in cm^2)   _____

2.4

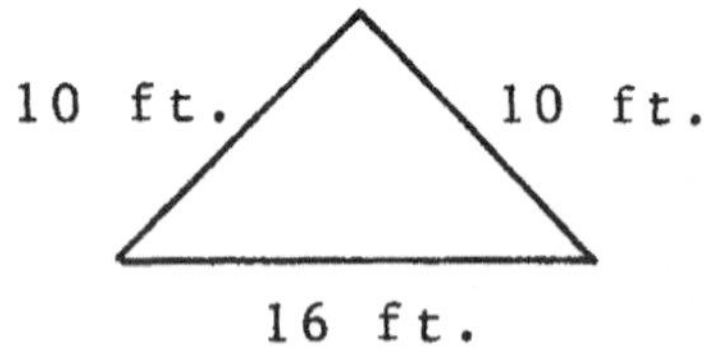

10 ft.   10 ft.   16 ft.

                                                          _____

DEFINITIONS

A *rectangle* is a plane geometric figure bounded by four sides with four right angles.

A *square* is a special case of a rectangle whose four sides are all equal lengths.

The rectangle is the most common plane figure found in building and construction trades. The applications in finding the areas of various rectangles are too numerous here to enumerate; however, knowing how to find the rectangular area is basic to any job.

Area of a rectangle: $A = a \times b$, where a and b are the lengths of two adjacent sides.

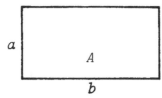

Area of a square: $A = a \times a = a^2$, where a is the length of any side, since all sides of a square are equal.

Model 1: Find the area of a rectangle whose adjacent sides are 6 cm and 10 cm.

$A = 6 \text{ cm} \times 10 \text{ cm} = 60 \text{ cm}^2$.

Model 2: Find the area of a square each of whose sides measures 4.5 ft. (express answer in meters).

$A = 4.5^2 = 20.25 \text{ ft.}^2$

Therefore, $A = 20.25 \times 9.29 \times 10^{-2} = 1.88 \text{ m}^2$.

▄▄▄▄ Find the areas of the following rectangles.

2.5 $a = 15$ cm; $b = 19.5$ cm.   _____

2.6 $a = 12$ ft.; $b = 12$ ft. (express answers
       in metric units).   _____

2.7 $a = 16$ cm; $b = 22$ cm (express answers
       in English units).   _____

▄▄▄▄ Write *true* or *false*.

2.8   _____ To find the area of a right triangle, multiply its
                 base by its altitude.

2.9   _____ Given the area of a triangle is 40 cm² , if its
                 altitude is 8 cm, its base is 15 cm.

17

Select your answer from the series of possible answers
provided after each of the following problems.

2.10   A rectangle has an area of 150 m². If one side is 25 m,
        the length of the adjacent side is _____.

        a. 60 m   b. 37.5 m   c. 0.6 m   d. 6 m

2.11   A square measures 6 inches on each side. Its area rounded
        off to the nearest whole number is _____.

        a. 232 cm²   b. 1,296 in.²   c. 91 cm²   d. 18 in.²

DEFINITION

A *trapezoid* is a four-sided geometric figure with two opposite
sides parallel and two opposite sides not parallel.

Area of a trapezoid: $A = \frac{1}{2}(a + b)h$, where
a and b are the lengths of the two parallel
sides and h is the altitude.

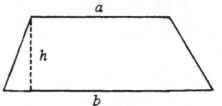

Model 1:   Find the area of a trapezoid whose
            parallel sides measure 12 m and
            18 m, and whose height is 10 m.

            $A = \frac{1}{2}(a + b)h = \frac{1}{2}(12 + 18)(10)$

            Therefore, $A = 150$ m².

Model 2:   The area of a trapezoid is 375 m².
            If the two parallel sides are 20 m
            and 30 m, respectively, what is the
            altitude of the trapezoid?

            $A = \frac{1}{2}(a + b)h$

            $375\,\text{m}^2 = \frac{1}{2}(20 + 30)h$

            $h = \dfrac{375}{\frac{1}{2}(50)}$

            Therefore, $h = 15$ m.

■■■■■ Find the required measurements of the following trapezoids.

2.12 a = 12 cm; b = 16 cm; h = 9 cm.
        Compute the area.   _____

2.13   A trapezoid has an altitude of 14 cm. Its parallel sides
        measure 5 and 8 cm, respectively. Its area is _____.

        a. 182 cm²   b. 91 cm²   c. 45.5 cm²   d. 280 cm²

⌣⌣⌣ PLANE FIGURES WITH CURVED BOUNDARIES ⌣⌣⌣⌣⌣⌣⌣⌣⌣⌣⌣⌣

   Circles are found in many building applications,
including cross sections of pipe, electrical
conduits, wiring, and culverts, to name a few.

+---+
| DEFINITION |
| |
| A *circle* is a plane figure bounded by a line, every point of|
| which is equally distant from a point within called the center.|
+---+

   Area of a circle: $A = \pi r^2 = \frac{1}{4}\pi d^2$, where
π = 3.14; r is the radius of the circle, and
d is the diameter of the circle. The more
common form of *pi*, 3.14, has been used to
compute the answers.

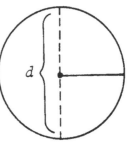

   Although the circumference of a circle
is not an area measurement, it is an imporant
measurement. The circumference is the distance
measured around the circle's boundary.

Circumference of a circle: $C = 2\pi r = \pi d$.

        Model 1:   Find the area of a circle whose
                   diameter is 14 in.

                   $A = \frac{1}{4}\pi d^2 = \frac{1}{4}(3.14)(14)^2$

                   Therefore, $A = 154$ in.²

        Model 2:   Find the area and circumference
                   of a circle whose radius is 6 cm.

                   $A = \pi r^2 = 3.14 (6)^2$

                   $A = 113.05$ cm²

                   $C = 2\pi r = 2(3.14)(6)$

                   $C = 37.68$ cm

19

█████ Find the areas of the following circles.

2.14 r = 4.5 cm   _____

2.15 d = 15 in.   _____

2.16   Circumference = 280 cm. (Hint: Find r
       from $C = 2\pi r$; then find area).   _____

2.17

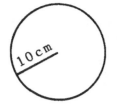

                                                       _____

2.18 r = 5 yd. (express answer in metric units).   _____

```
┌─────────────────────────────────────────────────────────────────┐
│                                                                   │
│  DEFINITION                                                       │
│                                                                   │
│  An ellipse is a plane figure bounded by a line formed by the     │
│  path of a point that moves so that the sum of its distances from │
│  two fixed points remains the same.                               │
│                                                                   │
└─────────────────────────────────────────────────────────────────┘
```

Area of an ellipse: $A = \pi ab$, where
a and b are the semiaxes of the ellipse.
In the figure shown, b is the major semiaxis,
the longer one, and a is the minor semiaxis.

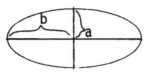

Model 1:   Find the area of an ellipse
           with a = 4 cm and b = 6 cm.

           $A = \pi ab = $ 3.14 (4)(6)

           A = 75.4 cm²

Model 2:   Find the area of an ellispe
           with major axis length of 15 cm
           and minor axis length of 8 cm.

           Since b = the major semiaxis, the
           major axis = $2b$.

           Therefore, $b = \frac{1}{2}(15) = 7.5$ cm.

           By the same reasoning, $a = \frac{1}{2}(8) = 4$ cm.

           $A = \pi ab = $ 3.14 (7.5)(4)

           A = 94.3 cm²

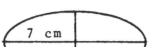 Find the areas of the following ellipses.

2.19 a = 4 in.; b = 7 in. (express answer in metric units).   _____

2.20 $2a$ = 10 cm; $2b$ = 20 cm.   _____

2.21

7 cm

4 cm

_____

⌣⌣⌣⌣⌣⌣⌣ **AREA APPLICATIONS** ⌣⌣⌣⌣⌣⌣⌣⌣⌣⌣⌣⌣⌣⌣⌣⌣⌣⌣⌣⌣

Now that you have developed a degree of competence in computing the areas of plane geometric figures, you will be exposed to practical applications of area computation. The applications are so numerous that a textbook or manual many times larger than this LIFEPAC would have to be used to cover all the possibilities. However, we shall be concentrating on a few of the more representative situations involved in the construction and building trades, such as carpentry, plumbing, masonry, and electrical work so that you may meet a number of the more common problems facing builders and tradesmen.

Carpentry. Lumber is normally sold by the *board foot*, which by definition is a piece of wood 1 inch thick, 12 inches wide, and 12 inches long. A slight complication enters into the picture, however, when you order a certain amount of lumber. Lumber comes in two sizes: nominal size (what you order), and actual size (what you get).

The reason for the variance is that *milling* (the process of cutting the wood lengthwise into smaller strips), and shrinkage due to drying, both reduce thickness and width by a small fraction. To be more specific, milling reduces the thickness of a one-inch board to $\frac{25}{32}$ inch; and wood two inches or greater in thickness is reduced $\frac{3}{8}$ of an inch by milling. Similarly, the width of wood is reduced by a predictable, specific amount. For all pieces 8 inches and less in width, the actual measure is $\frac{3}{8}$ inch less than what is ordered and paid for; and widths in excess of 8 inches are reduced by $\frac{1}{2}$ inch.

Model 1: You order twelve studs of 2" x 4" (translates into 2 inches thick by 4 inches wide) pine. What is the actual size you get?

The 2" thickness is reduced by $\frac{3}{8}$"; therefore, you get $2 - \frac{3}{8} = 1\frac{5}{8}$" in thickness.

Since 4" is less than 8", actual width is $4 - \frac{3}{8} = 3\frac{5}{8}$".

Model 2: You order five 2" x 10" boards, 6 feet in length, for shelving. What actual size in thickness and width did you receive?

Thickness $= 2 - \frac{3}{8} = 1\frac{5}{8}$".
Width $= 10 - \frac{1}{2} = 9\frac{1}{2}$".

Plywood is generally precut in sheets 4 feet wide by 8 feet long, and in varying thicknesses of $\frac{1}{2}$", $\frac{3}{4}$", or $\frac{5}{8}$". You need not be concerned with loss by milling or shrinkage with plywood.

PROCEDURE

To determine the amount of wood needed for a job requiring the covering of an area, determine the square footage of the area to be covered. Divide this area by the square footage of a single board or panel.

Model 1: You wish to panel your den. Two walls are 12 feet long and 8 feet high. The other two walls are 8' x 8'. How many panels of plywood are needed, assuming no wastage?

A (2 walls) $= 2 \times 12 \times 8 = 192$ ft.^{2}

A (2 walls) $= 2 \times 8 \times 8 = 128$ ft.^{2}

Total A (4 walls) $= 192 + 128 = 320$ ft.^{2}

A (each panel) $= 4 \times 8 = 32$ ft.^{2}

Number of panels needed $= \frac{320}{32} = 10$.

CONSUMER MATHEMATICS
5

LIFEPAC TEST

$$\frac{55}{69}$$

Name _____

Date _____

Score _____

CONSUMER MATHEMATICS 5: LIFEPAC TEST

Express the following measurements with the appropriate prefixes and symbols (each answer, 2 points).

1. 100 grams   _____

2. $\frac{1}{10}$ second   _____

Convert the following unit lengths as indicated (each answer, 3 points).

3. Convert 150 inches to centimeters.   _____

4. Convert 1,500 kilometers to miles.   _____

Convert the following unit areas as indicated (each answer, 3 points).

5. Convert 15 acres to hectares.   _____

6. Convert 50 square kilometers to
   square miles.   _____

Convert the following unit volumes as indicated (each answer, 3 points).

7. Convert 22 gallons (liq.) to liters.   _____

8. Convert 8 cubic yards to cubic
   meters.   _____

Convert the following unit weight as indicated (each answer, 3 points).

9. Convert 2,000 tons (short) to
   kilograms.   _____

Convert the following temperature as indicated (each answer, 4 points).

10. Convert 653°F to °C.   _____

Find the areas of the following geometric figures (each answer, 4 points).

11. Find the area of a rectangle if one side is 20 km and the other side is 25.5 km.

    _____

12. A circle has a radius of 6 in. What is its area?

    _____

Perform the following area applications (each answer, 4 points).

13. A culvert has a circumference of 280 cm. You wish to seal off both of its ends. How much material will you need?

    _____

14. You must cover a hole elliptical in shape. You measure the major and minor axes and find them to be 6 ft. and 4.5 ft. respectively. If you want a 6" overhang around the hole, how much covering will you need?

    _____

Compute the following volumes and surface areas (each answer, 4 points).

15. A rectangular solid has sides 16 cm, 12 cm, and 9 cm. What is its volume?

    _____

16. A pyramid has a rectangular base measuring 6' x 4'. If its altitude is 8', what is its volume?

    _____

17. Find the surface area of a sphere with a radius of 1 in.

    _____

18. Find the surface area of a cone whose base is a circle with a 5 cm radius and whose altitude is 10 cm.

    _____

19. Find the volume of a cylinder with an elliptical base that has a major axis of 6 cm, a minor axis of 5 cm, and an altitude of 12 cm.

    _____

2

20. Find the surface area of a cube whose side measures 15 cm.

_____

NOTES

Model 2: You wish to lay a subfloor for a room measuring $11\frac{1}{2}'$ x $8\frac{3}{4}'$. Although shrinkage of a board's thickness is not a problem in this case, the extent milling reduces the width is a problem since the board's width is one of the dimensions in determining the area covered by a board. Assume a standard length of 6' for each board. How many 1" x 3" x 6' boards will you need? (Hint: Milling reduces 3" by $\frac{3}{8}$"; 6' contain 72".)

A(room) = $11\frac{1}{2}$ x $8\frac{3}{4}$ = 100.625 ft.^{2}

A(each board) = $2\frac{5}{8}$ x 72 = 189 in.^{2} = 1.3125 ft.^{2}

Number of boards needed = $\frac{100.625}{1.3125}$ = 76.77 or 77.

<u>Concrete and Masonry</u>. In the construction and building trades, we are most often required to mix and pour cement in slabs, piers, or walls for footings and foundations. In laying brick, the mason is concerned with mixing mortar or grout to join the materials. Being able to figure areas, to work with ratios of materials in mixing cement, and to calculate the number of bricks or tiles needed to make a wall or finish a bathroom floor are all typical mathematics-related tasks.

Model 1: Determine the number of cement blocks needed to put up a wall measuring 20 meters in length and 2.5 meters in height. Each block is 10 cm x 20 cm.

A (wall) = 20 x 2.5 = 50 m^2

A (each block) = 10 x 20 x 10^{-4} = 0.02 m^2.

Number of blocks needed = $\frac{50}{0.02}$ = 2,500.

Model 2: You wish to seal up the ends of a culvert whose ends form circles measuring 24" in diameter each. You plan to use precut plywood to cap the ends and to plaster over the plywood to seal off the culvert. How much plywood will you need?

A (each culvert end) = $\frac{1}{4}\pi d^2$ = $\frac{1}{4}$(3.14)(24)^2

A = 452.16 in.^{2}

Therefore, plywood needed = 2 x 452.16 = 904.32 in.^{2}

Perform the following area applications.

2.22   Compute the number of vinyl tiles, measuring 25 cm each side, needed to tile a kitchen measuring 10½ ft. by 18 ft.   _____

2.23   If 400 bricks measuring 8½" by 3½" are required to build a wall 4½ ft. high, how long is the wall?   _____

2.24   A manhole measures 3' 4" in diameter. What is the area of a metal cover for the manhole, assuming a one-inch overhang around the circumference of the cover?   _____

2.25   You are going to convert a bedroom in your home to an office. You wish to cover the four walls with panel board (standard size 4' x 8') halfway up each wall, which measures 8 feet in height and 12 feet in length. Assuming no loss, how many panels will you need?   _____

Answer Questions 2.26 through 2.31 on the basis of the diagram shown.

Storage shed: one end is open, except for gable.

Construction: metal panels. Each side and end panel 6' high by 2' 6" wide. Each roof panel 4' 1" long by 2' 6½" wide. Each of 2 gable closures measures 1' 6" high by 7' 6" wide. Slanted roof sides each measure 4' ½".

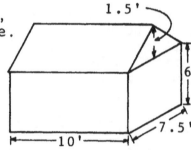

2.26   How many end and side panels are required?   _____

2.27   How many roof panels are required?   _____

2.28   How much area is covered by the two sides?   _____

2.29   How much area is covered by the enclosed end including its gable, and the gable at the open end?   _____

2.30   How much area is covered by the roof panels?   _____

2.31   What is the entire area covered by panels of all types?   _____

Answer Questions 2.32 through 2.37 based on the diagram shown.

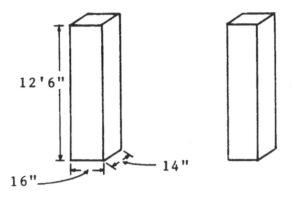

Task is to construct two brick columns of the dimensions shown on which an iron gate will eventually be hung. Because the bricks measure 8" long by 3½" wide by 2½" high, you decide to build each column by laying the bottom row of bricks as shown.

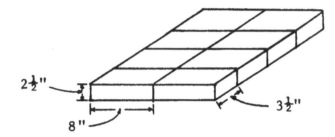

2.32   How much ground area will be covered by the first row of bricks laid as shown above?

_____

2.33   How many bricks high will it take to reach the top of a column?

_____

2.34   How many bricks are to be laid in each successive row?

_____

2.35   How many rows of bricks are required in each column?

_____

2.36   How many bricks are required in each column? In both columns?

_____
_____

2.37   What is the total surface area of each column, including top and bottom?

_____

Review the material in this section in preparation for the Self Test. This Self Test will check your mastery of this particular section as well as your knowledge of the previous section.

SELF TEST 2

Find the areas of the following plane figures (each answer, 4 points).

2.01   Compute the area of a triangle with a base of 15 cm and an altitude of 10.5 in. (answer in metric units).   _____

2.02   Find the altitude of a triangle whose area is 100 cm^2 and whose base is 20 cm.   _____

2.03   Given the following isosceles triangle, find its area.

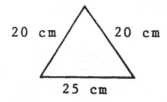

_____

2.04   A rectangle has adjacent sides measuring 15 ft. and 19.5 ft. Find its area in metric units.   _____

2.05   A trapezoid has the following dimensions: a = 25 cm, b = 35 cm, h = 10 cm. Find its area.   _____

2.06   A square measures 4 ft. on a side. Find the area in metric units.   _____

2.07   A circle has a radius of 8 cm. What is its area?   _____

2.08   Find the radius of a circle whose circumference measures 28 cm.   _____

2.09   An ellipse has a major axis of 14 cm and a minor axis of 10 cm. Find its area.   _____

2.010   Find the area of a circle whose circumference measures 100 cm.   _____

2.011   The ratio of the lengths of an ellipse is 3:2. If its area is 150 cm^2, what are the lengths of the major and minor semiaxes respectively?   _____

26

2.012   Given the figure shown, what is the area
         remaining in the square when you cut out the
         circle?

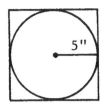

_____

Work the following area application problems (each answer, 4
points).

2.013   You are laying an asphalt driveway and parking area. How
         much surface area must you cover if the driveway and
         parking areas have the following dimensions?

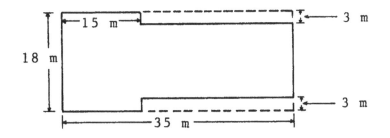

_____

2.014   What is the exposed surface area of the brass ring shown?

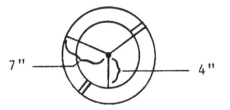

_____

2.015   You are given the job of laying carpet for a six-story
         building. At each floor the dimensions of the floor are
         75 meters in length by 40 meters in width. A stairwell
         takes up a space 2.5 m by 1.5 m, and cuts through each
         floor. If the rest of the floor area is to be carpeted,
         how much carpeting will you need?

_____

2.016   You are going to build a planter out of redwood. If the
         sides form trapezoids as shown, and the bottom forms
         a rectangle of the dimensions shown, how much redwood
         will you need?

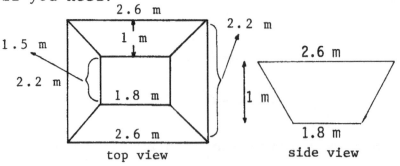

2.017   You own a swimming pool elliptical in shape. You wish
         to cover it at night to retain its warmth. If the pool
         measures 18 ft. across at its minor axis and 25 ft. across
         at its major axis, how much plastic material will you
         need to cover the pool, assuming you need a 1.5 ft. over-
         hang all around the pool?

2.018   You wish to paint a storage shed. Its four walls measure
         5 ft. high and 8 ft. wide each. If one gallon of paint
         covers 160 ft.^{2}, how many gallons of paint will you need?

58 / 72

Score _____
Teacher check _____
                Initial   Date

28

III. VOLUME COMPUTATIONS AND APPLICATIONS

OBJECTIVES

7. To identify solid geometric figures.
8. To compute volumes of liquids and solids given appropriate dimensions.
9. To estimate building materials requirements based on volume.

Once you have obtained mastery of area computations, you will find that determining the measurement of three-dimensional geometric figures is fairly straightforward. When we speak about quantatitive measuring of three-dimensional figures, we are concerned with measuring volume or capacity and surface area.

SOLID FIGURES WITH PLANE BOUNDARIES

This section will cover figures with plane boundaries. The cube, pyramid, and rectangular solid are included.

DEFINITION

A *cube* is a solid with six equal, square faces.

Volume of a cube: $V = a^3$, where a is the length of any side of a square face.

Surface area of a cube: $A = 6a^2$.

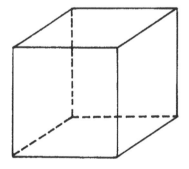

DEFINITION

A *rectangular solid* is a solid with three pairs of opposite, parallel faces, one pair of which are the ends.

29

Volume of a rectangular solid: $V = abc$, where a, b, and c are the lengths of the sides.

Surface area of a rectangular solid: $A = 2(ab + ac + bc)$.

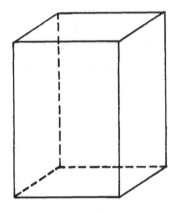

DEFINITION

A *pyramid* is a solid having triangular sides meeting in a point. Pyramids can have either rectangular or triangular bases.

Volume of a pyramid:
$V = \frac{1}{3}$(area of base) x (altitude).

The *surface area* found in the following formulas is the lateral surface area and excludes the area of any bases.

Surface area of a pyramid:
$A = \frac{1}{2}$(perimeter of base) x (slant height). Slant height is the altitude of one of the lateral (or side) triangles.

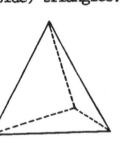

Tetrahedron
(Triangular Base Pyramid)

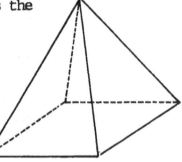

Rectangular Base Pyramid

Model 1: A cube measures 6 cm along one of its sides. What is its surface area?

$A = 6a^2 = 6(6)^2$

$A = 216$ cm^2

Model 2: A rectangular solid has sides measuring 5 meters, 7 meters, and 9 meters. What is its volume?

$V = abc = 5 \times 7 \times 9$

$V = 315$ m^3

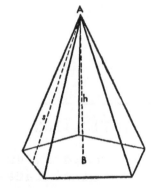

Pentagon Base Pyramid

■ Compute the following volumes and surface areas.

3.1   A rectangular pyramid has a base measuring 4 in. on each
        side and an altitude of 6 in. What is its volume?

        _____

3.2   A rectangular solid has sides of 4 cm, 6 cm, and 8 cm.
        What is its surface area?

        _____

3.3   A cube has a surface area of 96 in.² What is the length
        of its sides?

        _____

3.4   A pyramid composed of four equilateral triangles, called
        a *tetrahedron*, has a one-side length of 5 meters, and a
        slant height of 2.5√3 meters. What is its surface area?

        _____

3.5   A rectangular solid has sides of 15 in., 12 in., and
        9 in. What is its volume?

        _____

∿∿∿ SOLID FIGURES WITH CURVED BOUNDARIES ∿∿∿

The cylinder, sphere, and cone are figures
with curved boundaries. This section will present
measurements of these figures.

DEFINITION

A *cylinder* is a solid bounded by two equal, parallel circles
and a curved surface formed by moving a straight line of fixed
length so that its ends always lie on the two parallel circles.

Volume of a cylinder: V = (area of base) x (altitude);
$V = \pi r^2 h$.

Surface area of cylinder: A = (perimeter
of right section) x (lateral edge); $A = 2\pi rh$.

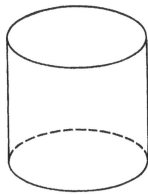

DEFINITION

A *sphere* is a round geometrical body whose surface is equally distant from the center at all points).

Volume of a sphere: $V = \frac{4}{3}\pi r^3$ or $V = \frac{1}{6}\pi d^3$

Surface area of a sphere: $A = 4\pi r^2$.

DEFINITION

A *cone* is a solid with a flat, round base that tapers evenly to a point at the top.

Volume of a cone: $V = \frac{1}{3}$(area of base) x (altitude).

Surface area of cone: $A = \pi r\sqrt{r^2 + h^2}$, where r = radius of the base, and h = altitude.

Model 1: Find the volume of a sphere with a diameter measuring 16 cm.
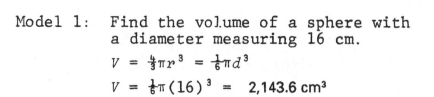
$V = \frac{4}{3}\pi r^3 = \frac{1}{6}\pi d^3$

$V = \frac{1}{6}\pi(16)^3 = 2,143.6\ cm^3$

Model 2: Find the surface area of a right
cylinder that has a circular
base with a radius of 3 cm and
whose altitude is 10 cm.

A = perimeter of right section x lateral edge

$A = 2\pi(3)(10) = \mathbf{188.4\,cm^2}$

Model 3: Find the amount of paint contained in a
can measuring 6 in. across the bottom
(diameter) and 8.5 in. high (answer in
liters).

$V = \pi r^2 h = \pi 3^2 \times 8.5$

$V = 240.4$ in.^{3}

But 1 in.^{3} = 0.0164 liter.

Therefore, (240.4) x (0.0164) = 3.94 liters.

Model 4: You are to paint the surface area of
a traffic control cone measuring 12
inches high and 9 inches across the
bottom, which is attached to a square
base measuring 9 inches on a side.
How much surface area will you need to
paint?

Two different area problems are involved:

1. surface area of cone with $r = 4.5''$ and
   $h = 12''$;

2. area of square 9" on a side, less the
   circumscribed area of a circle with
   radius of 4.5".

A (cone) $= \pi r \sqrt{r^2 + h^2} = \pi 4.5 \sqrt{4.5^2 + 12^2}$

$\qquad = \pi 4.5 \sqrt{164.25} = \pi 4.5 (12.82)$

$\qquad = 181.75$ in.^{2}

A of square - A of circle $= 9^2 - \pi(4.5)^2 = 17.41$ in.^{2}

Surface area of traffic cone = 181.15 + 17.41

$\qquad\qquad\qquad\qquad = 198.56$ in.^{2}

Find the volumes and surface areas of the figures listed below and solve the applications as required.

3.6   A pile of coal in the shape of a tetrahedron measures 3 meters along one of its base sides. The height of the pile measures 1.5 meters. How much coal is in the pile?

_____

3.7   What is the surface area of a rectangular solid whose sides are 4.5 cm, 6.8 cm, and 8.2 cm?

_____

3.8   What is the volume of a cone with a base radius of 3.5" and an altitude of 6.5" (answer in cubic meters)?

_____

3.9   Genesis 6:4 informs us of God's instructions to Noah regarding the construction of an ark:

    "This is to be its plan: the length of the ark shall be three hundred cubits, its breadth fifty cubits, and its height thirty cubits."

If a cubit measures an average of 20 inches (length of a forearm), what volume would Noah's ark contain? (answer in cubic meters). The shape of the ark was a rectangular solid.

_____

3.10   You are planning to construct a brick wall measuring 4.5 m in length, 1.2 m high, and 0.5 m in width. If a brick measures 20 cm x 9 cm x 5 cm, how many bricks will you need?

_____

3.11   The surface area of a cube is 660 in.^{2} What is the length of one of its sides? (answer in metric units)

_____

3.12   The standard baseball measures $2\frac{11}{16}$" in diameter. What is its volume?

_____

3.13   omitted

34

3.14   The diameter of a wrecking ball used to tear down buildings
        is 3.5 ft. Assuming a density of 0.26 $\frac{lb.}{in.^3}$ for the iron in
        the ball, what is the weight of the ball? (Hint: Find the
        volume of the sphere, convert to in.^{3}, and then multiply
        the result by the density.)

        _____

3.15   You are to paint the globe held aloft by the statue of
        Atlas. Its diameter is 10.5 ft. How much surface area
        must you cover with paint?

        _____

3.16   A swimming pool 35 ft. long and 20 ft. wide is filled to
        an average depth of 5 ft. How many gallons of water does
        the pool contain if a cubic foot holds 7½ gallons?

        _____

3.17   In Problem 3.16, how long will it take to fill the pool
        at a rate of 400 gallons per minute, rounded off to the
        nearest minute?

        _____

3.18   A steel reinforcing rod is 12 ft. long and ¾" thick at
        its diameter. If a cubic foot of steel weighs 490 lb.,
        how much does the rod weigh?

        _____

3.19   A plumber is laying pipe. His assistant digs a trench
        in roughly the shape of a rectangular solid measuring
        150 ft. in length, 9 inches deep along both sides, and
        12 inches wide at the top and bottom. How many cubic
        feet of earth must he remove?

        _____

3.20   In Problem 3.19, if the assistant's rate of pay is 75¢
        per cubic foot, how much should you pay him for his labor
        on the trench?

        _____

3.21   A driveway 18 ft. wide and 36 ft. long is to be paved with
        concrete 3 in. thick. How many cubic yards of concrete
        are required?

        _____

3.22   In Problem 3.21, if a mixture of 650 lb. of cement,
        1,300 lb. of sand, and 1,700 lb. of gravel make one cubic
        yard of concrete, how many pounds of each are needed for
        the driveway?

        _____

3.23   How many cement blocks are needed to construct a wall $\frac{3}{4}$ ft.
        thick, 6 ft. high, and 60 ft. long if it takes 10 standard
        cement blocks to make 1 cubic foot of wall?

        _____

3.24   In Problem 3.23, assuming the cost of cement blocks is
        $75 per 1,000, how much is the cost of the blocks for
        the wall to be constructed?

        _____

3.25   You are making a primary coil by wrapping copper wire
        around a metal rod. The rod is $\frac{1}{2}$" in diameter and 6"
        in length. If the wire is $\frac{1}{32}$" in diameter, how long a piece of
        wire is required to completely cover the rod?

        _____

        Answer Questions 3.26 through 3.30 based upon the diagram
        shown.

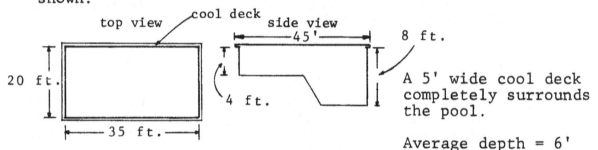

3.26   What are the approximate dimensions of the pool, exclusive
        of the cool deck?

        _____

3.27   Based on these dimensions, how much dirt will have to be
        excavated for the pool?

        _____

3.28   How much surface area is covered by the proposed cool deck?

        _____

3.29   If the cool deck is to be laid with concrete 3" thick, what volume of concrete will have to be poured?

_____

3.30   If a mixture of 24 lb. of cement, 48 lb. of sand, and 63 lb. of gravel is needed to make 1 cubic foot of concrete, how many pounds of each are needed to pour the cool deck?

_____

_____

_____

REVIEW   Before you take this last Self Test, you may want to do one or more of these self checks.

1. _____ Read the objectives. Determine if you can do them.
2. _____ Restudy the material related to any objectives that you cannot do.
3. _____ Use the SQ3R study procedure to review the material:
   a. **S**can the sections,
   b. **Q**uestion yourself again (review the questions you wrote initially),
   c. **R**ead to answer your questions,
   d. **R**ecite the answers to yourself, and
   e. **R**eview areas you didn't understand.
4. _____ Review all activities, and Self Tests, writing a correct answer for each wrong answer.

SELF TEST 3

Express the following measurements with the appropriate prefix symbols (each answer, 2 points).

3.01 $\frac{1}{1,000}$ liter   _____

3.02   1,000,000 tons   _____

3.03   10,000 cycles   _____

Convert the following unit lengths as indicated (each answer, 3 points).

3.04   Convert 500 feet to meters.   _____

3.05   Convert 120 meters to yards.   _____

3.06   Convert 1,000 centimeters to feet.   _____

Convert the following unit areas as indicated (each answer, 3 points).

3.07   Convert 25 square inches to square
         centimeters.   _____

3.08   Convert 1,000 square meters to
         square yards.   _____

3.09   Convert 250 hectares to acres.   _____

Convert the following unit volumes as indicated (each answer, 3 points).

3.010   Convert 50 liters to pints (dry).   _____

3.011   Convert 3 quarts (liq.) to cubic
         centimeters.   _____

3.012   Convert 100 cubic centimeters to
         fluid ounces.   _____

Convert the following unit weights as indicated (each answer, 3 points).

3.013   Convert 200 pounds to kilograms.   _____

3.014   Convert 1,000 grams to ounces.   _____

Convert the following temperature as indicated (this answer, 4 points).

3.015   Convert 1,500°C to °F.   _____

Find the areas of the following geometric figures (each answer, 4 points).

3.016   Find the area of a triangle with base
         of 6 m and altitude of 4 m.   _____

3.017   Find the area of a trapezoid whose
         parallel sides measure 8.5 m and
         4.5 m, and whose altitude is 6.5 m.   _____

3.018   An ellipse has a major semiaxis of
         20 cm and a minor semiaxis of 14 cm.
         What is its area?   _____

Perform the following area applications (each answer, 4 points).

3.019   Compute the square footage of carpet needed to cover a
        room 10' 6" x 12' 3".

_____

3.020   You are paneling an office that has 2 walls measuring
        18' x 8' and 2 walls measuring 9' x 8'. How many sheets
        of paneling will you need, assuming each panel sheet
        measures 4' x 8'?

_____

Find the volumes and surface areas of the following solid figures
(each answer, 4 points).

3.021   Find the surface area of a cube with sides of 5.5 cm each.

_____

3.022   A pyramid has an altitude of 4.7 in. and its base is a
        square with sides of 3.5 in. Find the pyramid's volume
        (answer in metric units).

_____

3.023   A rectangular solid has sides of 10 cm, 6.5 cm, and 8.3 cm.
        What is its volume?

_____

3.024   Find the volume of a cube whose sides each measure 3.2 cm.

_____

3.025   Given the rectangular solid shown, what is its surface
        area?

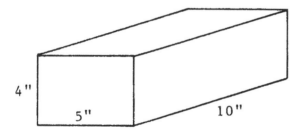

_____

3.026   A pyramid has a rectangular base measuring 3 meters long
        and 1.2 meters wide. Its slant height is 5.5 meters.
        Find the surface area of the pyramid.

_____

3.027   A cylinder has an elliptical base with major semiaxis
         length of 6 cm and minor semiaxis length of 4 cm. Its
         altitude is 7.5 cm. Find the volume of the cylinder.
         (Hint: Volume of the cylinder = area of base x altitude.)

         _____

3.028   A sphere has a radius of 4 inches. Find its surface area
         (answer in metric units).

         _____

3.029   A cone's altitude is 14 cm and its radius is 3.5 cm. Find
         its surface area.

         _____

3.030   A cone has a base with radius 5 inches. Its altitude is
         10 inches. Find its volume (answer in metric units).

         _____

3.031   A sphere has a radius of 3 inches. What is its volume?

         _____

3.032   Compute the volume of the cylinder shown:

         _____

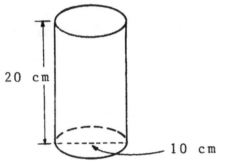

20 cm

10 cm

Solve the following solid figure application problems (each answer,
3 points).

3.033   How many liters of paint are contained in a can measuring
         8.5 inches across its base and 10 inches high?

         _____

3.034   You are to construct the following wall of cement block:

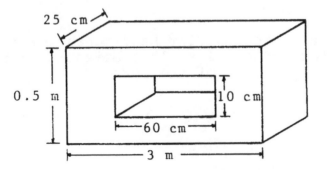

25 cm

0.5 m   10 cm

60 cm

3 m

Assume each cement block measures 10 cm long, 4 cm high, and 2 cm deep. How many blocks will you need? (Hint: Subtract the volume of the cut out portion from the total volume you would get if the wall had been solid originally).

_____

3.035   A can of oil has a surface area of 225 cm². If the can is 9.5 cm high, what is the diameter across its base?

_____

3.036   You have constructed wooden forms for pilings. The pilings are in the shape of rectangular solids, each measuring 20 ft. high and 2 ft. square. You are now going to pour cement into 10 of these forms. How much cement will you pour?

_____

3.037   You decide to build a pyramid in your back yard. If the pyramid is to have a slant height of 8 ft. and its perimeter is to be a perfect square measuring 4 ft. on each side, what will the total surface area of the pyramid be?

_____

```
┌──────────┐
│ 101   ╱  │
│    ╱     │
│  ╱   126 │
└──────────┘
```

Score   _____

✓ Teacher check _____
                             Initial   Date

Before taking the LIFEPAC Test, you may want to do one or more of these self checks.

1. _____ Read the objectives. Check to see if you can do them.
2. _____ Restudy the material related to any objective that you cannot do.
3. _____ Use the SQ3R study procedure to review the material.
4. _____ Review activities, Self Tests, and LIFEPAC Glossary.
5. _____ Restudy areas of weakness indicated by the last Self Test.

SCIENTIFIC NOTATION

> **PROCEDURE**
>
> An alternative method for writing numerals for either very large or very small numbers is known as *scientific notation*. A number is expressed in scientific notation when its numeral names a number that is greater than 1 but less than 10, and multiplied by some power of ten.

Model 1: Express 28,500,000 in scientific notation.
28,500,000 is 28.5 million.
But, 1 million = 10^6.
Therefore, 28.5 million may be expressed as
28.5×10^6.

Alternatively, $28,500,000 = 28.5 \times ?$

$$28.5 \overline{)28,500,000.0} \quad \begin{array}{c} 100,000.0 \end{array}$$

$1,000,000 = 10^6$
Therefore, $28,500,000 = 28.5 \times 10^6$, or 2.85×10^7 in scientific notation.

Model 2: Express 0.0000529 in scientific notation.
Move the decimal point five places to the right to obtain 5.29. However, to adjust for moving the decimal point five places to the right, you must multiply 5.29 by 10^{-5}.
Therefore, $0.0000529 = 5.29 \times 10^{-5}$.
in scientific notation.
Alternatively, $0.0000529 = 5.29 \times ?$

$$5.29 \overline{)0.0000529} \quad \begin{array}{c} .00001 \end{array}$$

$0.00001 = 10^{-5}$
Therefore, $0.0000529 = 5.29 \times 10^{-5}$.
in scientific notation.

GLOSSARY

altitude. The distance of a line drawn perpendicular from the base of a triangle to the intersection of the other two sides.

ampere. Rate of flow of charge of electricity.

base. Any side of a triangle.

circle. A plane figure bounded by a line, every point of which is equally distant from a point within called the center.

cone. A solid with a flat, round base that tapers evenly to a point at the top.

cube. A solid geometric figure with six equal, square faces.

cylinder. A solid bounded by two equal, parallel circles and a curved surface formed by moving a straight line of fixed length so that its ends always lie on the two parallel circles.

ellipse. A plane figure bounded by a line formed by the path of a point that moves so that the sum of its distances from two fixed points remains the same.

international metric system. A decimal system of weights and measures, employing grams, meters, liters, and other units.

mensuration. Branch of mathematics dealing with finding lengths, areas, and volumes.

milling. Process in carpentry of cutting lumber lengthwise into smaller strips.

pyramid. A solid having triangular sides meeting in a point.

rectangle. A plane geometric figure bounded by four sides with four right angles.

rectangular solid. A solid geometric figure with three pairs of opposite, parallel faces, one pair of which are the ends.

sphere. A round geometrical body whose surface is equally distant from the center at all points.

square.   A special case of a rectangle whose four sides are all
     of equal lengths.

trapezoid.   A four-sided geometric figure with two opposite sides
     parallel and two opposite sides not parallel.

triangle.   A plane geometric figure bounded by three sides and
     enclosed by three angles.